Plymouth Colony, Massachusetts

A SCAVENGER HUNT

By Barbara Tibbetts

Whooo's up for a challenge? Find all 30 items pictured in the book

A L👁👁k Book

ISBN: 978-1-944489-16-8

JOHN AND PRISCILLA ALDEN
FAMILY SITES

HAS BEEN DESIGNATED A

NATIONAL HISTORIC LANDMARK

THIS SITE POSSESSES NATIONAL SIGNIFICANCE
IN COMMEMORATING THE HISTORY OF THE
UNITED STATES OF AMERICA

LONGFELLOW'S 1858 POEM *THE COURTSHIP OF MILES STANDISH* ABOUT
THE ROMANCE OF *MAYFLOWER* PASSENGERS JOHN ALDEN AND PRISCILLA
MULLINS BECAME ONE OF AMERICA'S MOST POPULAR NATIONAL ORIGIN
STORIES. THIS CA.1700 HOUSE BECAME THE FOCUS OF DESCENDANTS'
PRIDE IN TELLING THE ALDEN STORY TO SUCCESSIVE GENERATIONS.

2008

NATIONAL PARK SERVICE
UNITED STATES DEPARTMENT OF THE INTERIOR

Geneology

The Mayflower passengers John and Priscilla Alden made their home in Duxbury. Add a sticker when you find this homestead.

Place a sticker HERE

The National Monument to the Forefathers

The National Monument to the Forefathers, formerly known as the Pilgrim Monument, was dedicated to the Mayflower settlers in 1889. Standing 81 feet tall is the largest free- standing, granite monument in the world. Add a sticker when you find this monument.

Place a sticker HERE

Religious Freedom

The Pilgrims founded the congregation of the First Parish Church of Plymouth in 1620 to realize their dream of freedom of belief. This church was placed on the National Register of Historic Places in 2014. Add a sticker when you discover this beautiful door way.

Place a
sticker
HERE

WILLIAM BRADFORD
GOVERNOR AND HISTORIAN
OF THE
PLYMOUTH COLONY

BORN IN AUSTERFIELD, ENGLAND-1590
DIED IN PLYMOUTH, NEW ENGLAND-1657

Governor Bradford

William Bradford signed the Mayflower Compact upon arriving in Massachusetts in 1620. He was the longtime governor of the Plymouth Colony settlement. Add a sticker when you find this granite memorial.

Place a sticker HERE

Oldest Museum

Pilgrim Hall houses the founding story of America and is the Nations's oldest continuously-operating museum. The museum has artifacts from the original voyage of the Mayflower. Add a sticker when you find this museum and take a look inside.

Place a sticker HERE

Beaver Hat

Steeple-crowned hats were popular with both men and women in Western Europe in the 17th century. This particular hat was owned by Constance Hopkins. Add a sticker when you find this hat.

Place a sticker HERE

WHITE CRADLE

1620 | According to tradition, Susanna and William White brought this cradle from Holland in anticipation of the birth of their child. Their son Peregrine, meaning "traveler" or "Pilgrim," was born on board the *Mayflower* in Provincetown Harbor in November of 1620. He was the first child born to the Pilgrims in America (Oceanus Hopkins was born during the Atlantic crossing).

The hooded wicker cradle is typical of those made in Holland. Similar cradles can be seen in period paintings by Dutch artists.

This cradle is a symbol of the Pilgrims' commitment to staying in America and raising their families.

Family

This cradle was brought from Holland on the Mayflower by Susanna and William White in anticipation of the birth of their son. He was the first child born to the Pilgrims on board the Mayflower. Add a sticker when you find this cradle.

Place a sticker HERE

Go to www.thelookbookhunt.com to find out more!

PIECE OF PLYMOUTH ROCK
Gift of the Plymouth Antiquarian Society, 1983

Please touch!

The Look Book

A Piece of the Rock

Curious? Please touch! Provided by the Plymouth Antiquarian Society this piece of Plymouth Rock is available for you to touch. Add a sticker when you find this piece of Plymouth Rock.

Place a sticker HERE

Finding a New Home!

The Pilgrims seeking religious freedom set sail
on the Mayflower from Holland in July of 1620.
Add a sticker when you find this replica and
climb aboard the Mayflower II.

Place a
sticker
HERE

Go to www.thelookbookhunt.com to find out more! **19**

D.A.R.

This monument was erected in 1920 by the
National Society of the Daughters of the
American Revolution in memory of the heroic
women of 1620 aboard the Mayflower. Add a
sticker when you find this statue.

Place a
sticker
HERE

1620

This rock is an American symbol of freedom and is viewed by over one million visitors a year! Add a sticker when you find this rock.

Place a sticker HERE

Massasoit

The term Massasoit means Great Sachem.
Great Sachem translated means great
leader. Massasoit was the great leader of the
Wampanoag tribe. Add a sticker when you find
the statue of Massasoit.

Place a
sticker
HERE

Remembering

"This Monument Marks the First Burying Ground in Plymouth of the Passengers of the Mayflower..." Add a sticker when you find this inscription.

Place a sticker HERE

NATIONAL DAY OF MOURNING

Since 1970, Native Americans have gathered at noon on Cole's Hill in Plymouth to commemorate a National Day of Mourning on the U.S. Thanksgiving holiday. Many Native Americans do not celebrate the arrival of the Pilgrims and other European settlers. To them, Thanksgiving Day is a reminder of the genocide of millions of their people, the theft of their lands, and the relentless assault on their culture. Participants in National Day of Mourning honor Native ancestors and the struggles of Native peoples to survive today. It is a day of remembrance and spiritual connection as well as a protest of the racism and oppression which Native Americans continue to experience.

Erected by the Town of Plymouth on behalf of the United American Indians of New England

Respect

The National Day of Mourning can remind us that respecting each other's differences will create a more peaceful world. Add a sticker when you find this plaque.

Place a sticker HERE

Heritage

The 18th century home was originally built by Edward Winslow, great-grandson of the Pilgrim Edward Winslow. Add a sticker when you find this house and discover its rich history.

Place a
sticker
HERE

The Beginning of America

This memorial is a tribute to America's first immigrants. The eagle is placed on top as a reminder of the freedoms the immigrants were looking for when they came to America. Add a sticker when you find this tribute.

Place a sticker HERE

Go to www.thelookbookhunt.com to find out more!

America's first street and site
of the home of William Brewster,
the Pilgrims' spiritual leader.
Formerly First Street, its name
was changed to Leyden Street in honour
of the city in the Netherlands
that offered refuge to the Pilgrims.

First Street

First street was named Leyden Street in 1823 after the city in Holland that offered the Pilgrims refuge before coming to America. This street is the oldest continuously inhabited street in New England. Add a sticker when you find this street.

Place a sticker HERE

Go to www.thelookbookhunt.com to find out more!

Pilgrims Lived Here

The Jabez Howland House is the only house left in Plymouth where the Pilgrims actually lived! Add a sticker when you find this house.

Place a sticker HERE

Oldest House

The house which holds this window was
built around 1640 by Richard Sparrow, an
Englishman who arrived in Plymouth in 1636.
Add a sticker when you find the windows of the
oldest house in Plymouth.

Place a
sticker
HERE

A Working Grist Mill

This grist mill is a reproduction of the original 1636 Jenney Grist Mill and stands on the site of the original mill. This corn grinding water-powered mill allowed the colonists to no longer grind corn by hand. Add a sticker when you find this working grist mill.

Place a sticker HERE

Go to www.thelookbookhunt.com to find out more!

1677

The Harlow Old Fort House was the original residence of William Harlow. This house was made from salvaged material taken from the Pilgrim's fort-house on Burial Hill. Add a sticker when you find this house on the National Register of Historical Places.

Place a sticker HERE

Defense

This two story fort, known as a blockhouse, allowed the Pilgrims to defend themselves from various directions. What will you find when you climb the stairs to the second level? Add a sticker when you find this blockhouse.

Place a sticker HERE

Wampanoag Homesite

Imagine living here! The Wampanoag tribe lived in homes like this along the coast during the growing season. Add a sticker when you find this home.

Place a sticker HERE

Go to www.thelookbookhunt.com to find out more!

Mishoon

The definition of Mishoon is a canoe made by digging out a log. The Wampanoag used fire to hollow out the log to make the Mishoon. Add a sticker when you find a Mishoon.

Place a sticker HERE

Protection

The Pilgrims feared that the French, Spanish, unfriendly natives, or pirates might attack the colony. They brought with them several different types of cannons and housed them in the fort on the hill to protect the town. Add a sticker when you see a cannon.

Place a
sticker
HERE

Go to www.thelookbookhunt.com to find out more!

NEAR THIS SITE
THE NAUSET TRIBE
OF THE
WAMPANOAG NATION

SEEKING TO PROTECT THEMSELVES
AND THEIR CULTURE
HAD THEIR

FIRST ENCOUNTER

8 DECEMBER 1620

WITH
MYLES STANDISH, JOHN CARVER,
WILLIAM BRADFORD,
EDWARD WINSLOW, JOHN TILLEY,
EDWARD TILLEY,
JOHN HOWLAND, RICHARD WARREN,
STEPHEN HOPKINS,
EDWARD DOTEY, JOHN ALLERTON,
THOMAS ENGLISH,
MASTER MATE CLARK,
MASTER GUNNER COPIN
AND THREE SAILORS
OF THE MAYFLOWER COMPANY

THIS TABLET IS PLACED IN 2001 BY THE SOCIETY OF COLONIAL WARS
IN THE COMMONWEALTH OF MASSACHUSETTS

First Encounter Beach

The first encounter between the Pilgrims and members of the Nauset Tribe of the Wampanoags took place at this beach, arrows flew and shots were fired. Add a sticker when you find this beach.

Place a sticker HERE

Go to www.thelookbookhunt.com to find out more!

1620   1920

SIXTEEN PILGRIMS
LED BY
MYLES STANDISH WILLIAM BRADFORD
STEPHEN HOPKINS AND EDWARD TILLEY
FOUND THE PRECIOUS INDIAN CORN
ON THIS SPOT WHICH THEY CALLED

CORN HILL

NOVEMBER 16 1620
OLD STYLE

AND SURE IT WAS GODS GOOD PROVIDENCE
THAT WE FOUND THIS CORN FOR ELSE WE
KNOW NOT HOW WE SHOULD HAVE DONE

MOURT'S RELATION

PROVINCETOWN TERCENTENARY
COMMISSION

John F. Paramino Sculp.   Boston Mass

Corn Hill Beach

It was near this beach in 1620 a group of 16 Pilgrims came upon a Wampanoag stash of corn and fresh water which they took and used to sustain their people. Add a sticker when you find this plaque.

Place a sticker HERE

Go to www.thelookbookhunt.com to find out more!

Arrived!

In November 1620 the pilgrims first landed in Provincetown. Here they created the Mayflower Compact and spent 5 weeks exploring the tip of Cape Cod before continuing onto Plymouth. Add a sticker when you find this plaque.

Place a sticker HERE

Pilgrim Monument

The Pilgrim Monument was built between 1907 and 1910 to commemorate the first landing of the Mayflower Pilgrims' in the New World. Add a sticker when you find this monument.

Place a sticker HERE

Aquinnah Massachusetts

The Wampanoags considered the land of great importance and treated it with great care and enjoyed the beauty of Aquinnah on Marthas Vineyard. Add a sticker when you find this amazing view.

Place a sticker HERE

Plymouth, Massachusetts

Plymouth, Massachusetts was known as the location of the first Thanksgiving and holds a special place in history. In September 1620, a brave group of 102 men, women and children set sail from Plymouth, England to start a new life searching for religious freedom. The colonists who traveled for a treacherous 66 days on the ship called the Mayflower are known as "Pilgrims."

They first came to America at the tip of Cape Cod, in Provincetown. Onboard, the ship off the coast of Provincetown they created and signed the Mayflower Compact on November 11, 1620. The Mayflower compact was a new set of rules to allow the Pilgrims as they are now known, to govern themselves. One month later, the Mayflower crossed Massachusetts Bay to arrive in Plymouth harbor.

Only 53 Pilgrims survived the long journey and first winter aboard the Mayflower in Plymouth harbor. Once on land, with the guidance of the Wampanoag Indians, the Pilgrims prepared for the next winter, planting and harvesting crops, extracting sap, catching fish and learning what the land has to offer. With much to celebrate a feast was prepared which lasted 3 days.

Celebrating a fall harvest was an English tradition and is now known as "Thanksgiving." Guests at the first Thanksgiving included Wampanoag Indians, their leader Massasoit and Squanto their appointed translator and the 53 surviving Pilgrims.

Rules of Engagement

As you discover historic Plymouth
Colony with "The LOOK Book," add
a sticker when you locate the item
pictured. It is fun to compete in
teams. Purchase several books and
see who can complete the entire
book, or set a time limit and see who
finds the most items pictured.
HAPPY HUNTING!

Barbara Tibbetts *is the author and creator of The LOOK Book series. She
is a former kindergarten teacher, the mother of three children and divides her time
between Acton, MA and the Island of Nantucket. The first book in the series was
developed for Barbara's daughter on a trip to Nantucket with her brownie troop
to engage the girls and teach them about the island.*

Made in the USA
Monee, IL
04 March 2020

22501654R00040